SAM
THE FIREHOUSE
CAT

Story and Pictures
by
VIRGINIA PARSONS

gb GOLDEN PRESS • NEW YORK

Second Printing, 1971

ENGINE COMPANY NO. 9.

Just down the street in the firehouse lives a very fine cat. His name is Sam. Sparky the dog is his friend. *Clang clang* goes the fire alarm. And Sparky and Sam know exactly what to do.

Sam dashes upstairs, as fast as he can.
Sparky jumps onto his seat in the hose truck.

Sam watches

while the motors roar...

...the bells clang...the sirens scream...
and off go the engines to the fire.
The doors slam shut and Sam is alone.

He rushes
to the
window to see where the engines
are going.
But today Sam can
hardly see anything,
the air is so
full of smoke.

Horrors! The fire is right across the street
at the warehouse. And in the warehouse
live Mrs. Catz and her daughter Becky.

Sam
must save
them!

The quickest way out
is down the pole.
Sam jumps...grabs the pole...
wraps his paws around it and
tucks up his tail.

Z
i
p
.
.
p
.
.
.
p
.
.
.
p
.
.
p

p

p

p

p

p

Then down
he
goes.

It's a good thing that cats can get through small spaces. There is just barely room for Sam to squeeze under the door. It's another good thing that Sam knows a short cut to get to the burning warehouse.

Poor Mrs. Catz and Becky! They have
been driven up to the roof by the smoke
and flames. They are clinging to each
other, crying and coughing.

Sam runs down the alley as fast as
he can. The warehouse is burning
fiercely. But on the building next
door there is a staircase.

There is not a moment to lose.
Sam dashes up the steps. The smoke
is getting thicker. Hurry, Sam, hurry!

Sam reaches the roof. He sees a board
across the space between the buildings.
Poor Mrs. Catz couldn't see it because
of all the smoke. She and Becky
are too frightened to move.

"Follow me," says Sam. "Watch
my ears and don't look down."
Mrs. Catz and
Becky do exactly
as Sam tells them.
They follow
Sam's ears
and
don't look
down
even once,
and soon they
are safely across.
Sam has saved
eighteen lives, for
cats have nine lives
each, you know.

Mrs. Catz and Becky go to the firehouse
with Sam. They are all sooty and thirsty and
Mrs. Catz' whiskers are singed. But they are safe.

Sam gets a medal for being such a
brave cat. He is a hero.

In fact, Becky thinks
he is the most wonderful
cat in the world.

Now the warehouse is repaired after the fire.
Mrs. Catz must go back to her job.

But Becky stays with Sam, her hero.
They get married right away, and Sam teaches
Becky to slide down the pole, too.

Soon there are kittens
in the family.
They all learn
pole-sliding, too.

Z
I
P
!

And one day, if you are
very lucky, you may see them
all, at the firehouse
just down the street.